# Alice in I.D.25

## A Codebreaking Parody of
## *Alice's Adventures in Wonderland*

By Frank Birch, Dilly Knox & G.P. Mackeson

Introductions by Mavis Batey & Edward Wakeling

# Introduction

Timed to coincide with a brand-new exhibition about codebreaking and intelligence in World War One, the Bletchley Park Trust is delighted to reproduce this unique parody of *Alice's Adventures in Wonderland*. Originally written by codebreakers Frank Birch and Dilly Knox at the end of World War One, it was performed privately as a pantomime in London in December 1918.

Unseen for decades, it was not until 2007 that Edward Wakeling (a Lewis Carroll expert) and Mavis Batey MBE (a World War Two codebreaker herself who worked for Dilly Knox at Bletchley Park) brought this fascinating script back to life and provided new introductions. The extract below from the 2007 booklet highlights their sources:

> We consulted two copies; the first had remained among the private papers of one of the co-writers, Dilly Knox. His son, the late Oliver Knox, very kindly made this available to us. Unfortunately, a few pages were missing, but a second copy, among the papers of Alexander Guthrie Denniston, yielded access to the gaps (ref. DENN 3/3). The Denniston archive is now housed at the Churchill Archives Centre ... In an appendix we include a parody of *Jabberwocky* by Dilly Knox written around 1940 [The National Archives, HW3/171].

Offering thanks to them for reviving it, and to the Churchill Archives Centre for supplying some of the original images, the Bletchley Park Trust hopes to complement its visitors' World War One experience with this clever piece of writing by some of Great Britain's first codebreakers.

# The Codebreaking Context

## by Mavis Batey

Lewis Carroll's *Alice* is renowned for her candid opinions and shrewd assessments of people and institutions. She had already parodied the political scene in Saki's *The Westminster Alice* before she set about penetrating the secret world of Intelligence. *Alice in I.D.25* was written at the end of the First World War for the entertainment of the staff. Frank Birch, who wrote the text, and Dilly Knox, the poems, were two of its most colourful characters and shared a house in Chelsea where the pantomime was secretly performed.

Frank Birch                               Dilly Knox

The first official British Secret Service Bureau was set up in 1909 for espionage and counter-espionage, the forerunner of MI5 and MI6. In 1914 signals intelligence, the art of reading the enemy's wireless traffic, would, however, become a new and more powerful potential secret weapon as Winston Churchill, the first Sea Lord*, foresaw. The Admiralty had cut the underwater cables belonging to the Germans on the first day of the war, which forced them to communicate on the airwaves. When these secret encoded messages were intercepted and sent to the Admiralty there was a frantic search for the right sort of people able to decode them and Alice had now stumbled in on them in their Whitehall hideout.

It was not for nothing that the first creature she met was the White Rabbit, whom she knew from previous adventures. He was now 'obviously very important' and as usual in a great hurry. He was Frank

---

*   The appointment held by Churchill at this time was in fact First Lord of the Admiralty (the political head of the Royal Navy), the First Sea Lord being its professional head. Nonetheless, Churchill was indeed in a position to influence and encourage the development of signals intelligence.

Adcock, formerly Ancient Historian and Lay Dean of King's College, Cambridge, who was largely responsible for getting his fellow Kings' men, Birch and Knox, into Room 40, later to become I.D.25. His friends describe him as a small round man with twinkling eyes behind thick glasses. Germany and France had recruited servicemen for the new role of official cryptographers, but here from the beginning it was decided that it was men of the 'professor type' who were needed.

Alice lost sight of the White Rabbit through the arches of the Old Admiralty Building and found herself falling down some sort of tube into a wire basket where there was someone waiting to remove the shuttle full of gobbledegook messages that had accompanied her in her fall. There were still tubists employed in a similar capacity twenty years later at Bletchley Park. The cryptographers worked shifts which, now being naval, the dons had to call watches. One 'little man' seated at a desk in the far corner of the room by the window was watching what was going on very carefully. Alice learned later that he never left his post and had a bed brought in beside him. This was Commander Alastair Denniston, one of the first recruits to Room 40, who had been a language instructor at Osborne College on the Isle of Wight. So he had some pretensions to being naval. He would see codes and ciphers resolutely through during the inter-war years to become Head of Bletchley Park where he was still called the 'little man' by old friends.

Alice was soon rescued and asked what group she belonged to but she had no idea about discriminants and such like in the preambles of messages and was told in that case she must be either NSL or Baltic, and if the latter she must be given to the Watch. The codebreakers woke up at once and howled, 'We don't do Baltic. We won't do Baltic.' She was then told, 'Very well, you'd better go with NSL,' and she was dropped rather roughly onto a heap of papers in a big tin, and more were thrown on her until she was completely buried. We have to turn to the 'little man's' memoirs to find out what NSL was all about.

Alastair Denniston

All messages had to be marked either 'logged' or 'sent,' otherwise they had to be bundled into a tin on which a large black NSL meaning 'neither logged nor sent' was painted. Alice was terrified that she might be buried in NSL but eventually she managed to climb to the top of the papers. It seems that when the war was over, according to Denniston, there was still a box called NSL when there had been no log for the last two years. Birch was determined to get the dig in about the neglect of Baltic as he was in charge of the traffic.

Alice was hoping to meet the DIND that the White Rabbit had talked about as she gathered that he was the boss. But she would have to wait until the end of her adventures to come face to face with the Director of Naval Intelligence or the DNI as he was officially called. 'Blinker' Hall, appointed by Churchill in 1914, was a larger than life character and had a habit of blinking frequently, hence his name. He was in charge of all aspects of naval intelligence including traditional cloak and dagger spying and, after 1916, the up and coming codebreaking in Room 40. However, he thought his authority would be increased if their naval work could be extended to the diplomatic field. This proved a godsend as confidence in naval codebreaking suffered a setback when their intelligence was misinterpreted, denying the country a decisive victory at Jutland in 1916. They were still simmering about the cock-up during Alice's visit and Humpty Dumpty, who was as fat as ever in spite of rationing, had apparently just returned from a mission to do, by sheer weight, 'what neither Jellicoe nor Beatty could do – to sink the German fleet.'

At the beginning of 1917, however, Room 40 was dealt a trump card when Nigel de Grey, the Dormouse, who handled Hall's diplomatic traffic, broke a telegram from Zimmermann, the German Foreign Minister, to the Mexican government. Zimmermann offered support for Mexican claims to the territory of Arizona and Texas if they launched an attack on the United States. Our Foreign Secretary was 'over the moon'

Nigel de Grey

as there was now every chance that this might bring America into the war. When this did indeed happen in April, 'Blinker' Hall and de Grey celebrated with champagne, but the DNI had to spin the Zimmermann telegram as the work of an agent to protect the real source. This cover-up was also used later at Bletchley Park when Enigma decodes were referred to as 'Boniface telegrams' to protect the great Ultra secret source. The Dormouse, although elated by his success, had to keep very quiet about it all. When Alice met him later he was 'much larger than he used to be and wore a coronet' and his colleagues still resented the way he kept himself to himself. 'He does his own work and minds his own business. We don't want that sort of thing here,' they said and pushed him out of the room. He was in fact just about to be sent abroad to organise Mediterranean intelligence, but many of the creatures would meet up with him again when he became a key figure at Bletchley Park in the next war.

'Blinker' Hall, with his arm strengthened, decided to reorganise signals intelligence to make it more effective to commanders at sea and prevent another Jutland. In May 1917 he increased the staff and moved them from Room 40 into a set of rooms nearby, which would henceforth be known as section 25 of his Naval Intelligence Division, and it was in I.D.25 that Alice now found them all. The layout was most confusing; there was a range of rooms seemingly from 45–56 but none of the numbers appeared to have anything to do with each other. The DNI appointed Captain James to run I.D.25 to see that in future its intelligence would be co-ordinated with operational command. James, who never lived down Millais's painting of him blowing bubbles as a child which Pears used for a soap advertisement, was, as Alice learned, 'a nice chap man – knows 'is place.' However, Alice could not understand why she didn't meet him as his hours were apparently 10–7 and 7–10. Humpty Dumpty praised his ability to pour oil on troubled waters provided he was given the right oil. Captain James must have also impressed those in authority as he went on to become an Admiral in 1938 in charge of co-ordinating intelligence in preparation for the next war.

Alice was taken to see the Waterflap who had just arrived breathless from a long flight to start work right away on an 'appreciation' of the messages that had been logged for him. Alice, who had been paying great attention to the workings of signals intelligence, observed that his clerk was carrying out the same procedure as the creature at the receiving end of the tube – but she hadn't appreciated that this was not logging for decoding purposes but for traffic analysis. A great deal could be learned from the wireless itself without making sense of the gobbledegook – call signs, operator's chitchat, repeat transmissions, or standard messages at the same hour such as weather forecasts, were only a part of it. 'Nobby' Clarke, with a legal training and knowledge of German, had been employed for this type of traffic analysis by 'Blinker' Hall in 1916. As soon as the Waterflap arrived he spotted a very important message prefixed with ssd (sehr sehr dringend) and another which got him very excited saying KR KR KR signifying Kriegstelegram which a German operator would send out to clear the air for an important announcement. 'The Fleet's out,' yelled the Waterflap. 'Send for Captain James. Send for the DIND. Send for the King,' and then seeing Alice idly standing by ordered her to take the message to the Directional Room. Here traffic analysis would be combined with cross bearings provided by a network of a number of direction-finding stations that could locate the fleet or submarines as they left port. Alice was highly intrigued by the 'plotting' on a high table where they were playing a kind of game with little pieces of string with weighted ends. Submarine tracking apparatus would be rather more sophisticated in the next war. Nobby Clarke would then be in overall charge of the Naval Section at Bletchley Park in close contact with Frank Birch, who ran Hut 4, the section which dealt with intelligence from Hut 8 where the German naval messages were broken; also with Dilly Knox who broke the Italian Enigma naval code which led to the success of the Battle of Matapan.

Dilly Knox was a great Carroll devotee, and appropriately appeared as the Dodo in the pantomime, as Lewis Carroll saw himself in that guise in *Alice's Adventures in Wonderland*. Alice learned straight away that he was a classicist, particularly fond of Greek. Alice's father, the Dean of Christ Church, had produced the standard Liddell and Scott Greek lexicon so she was very familiar with Greek scholars. Dilly was best known at Kings as a papyrologist and had spent months on end commuting to the British Museum trying to piece together fragments of the Herodas mimes unearthed from the desert. He approached cryptography with the same determination, feel for language and inspired guesswork. Dilly's brother was working beside him when Alice met him and she couldn't understand why Dilly said he was 'a Roman.' He was the famous Ronald Knox, budding detective story writer, who was about to become a Roman Catholic priest, much to their father, the Bishop of Manchester's displeasure.

The Dodo had just pulled off a triumph and showed Alice his work, 'three letter stuff, you see,' he said modestly. Cracking the Admiral's flag code, which gave orders to submarines, had been a priority to save the Atlantic convoys, especially after America came into the war. The Zeppelins also signalled their positions to the flag-ship, so that, all in all, when Dilly broke the 'three letter stuff' in the summer of 1917, it was of equal importance to the Dormouse's breaking of the Zimmermann telegram earlier in the year. For this the DNI had earned a knighthood.

Following this new triumph Captain Hall became a Rear Admiral and Dilly plodded on with the next problem.

To assist him in his vital work he was given a lady secretary, which caused problems as Room 53, where he worked, was tiny and had the only bath in the Admiralty in it. Dilly was much addicted to solving puzzles in a soapy bath and in one of his poems jokes that the 'sailor in Room 53, has never, it's true, been to sea [except in Birch's yacht] but though not in a boat, he has yet served afloat – in a bath at the Admiralty.' Dilly worked his own hours and often through the night, whatever watch he was meant to be keeping, but his secretary worked office hours and he had to rush to get dressed before she arrived. He married Miss Roddam soon after the war ended. At the end of Alice's interview the Dodo 'doddered' past her muttering, 'I must go to Room 40 and find fault with things.' The Director now occupied the old Room 40 and Dilly, who always thought that things would be better without administrative window-dressers, as he called them, found plenty to complain about. He was well known for his habit of sending in resignations, knowing that these could never be accepted.

The announcement that the war was over actually came through while Alice was in I.D.25. It was then that at last she came face to face with the White Rabbit's DIND, who was banked by his two smart personal assistants, Lord Hershel on his right and Claud Serocold on the left. Rear Admiral, Sir William Hall, obviously very well pleased with himself, appeared with a broad grin on his face in the guise of a jubilant turkey cock. Alice then learned why they always called him DIND; it was short for Dindon. 'It's French, you see,' they told her. The DNI had a tray of flags to decorate everyone within sight. But when the creatures heard that some would have to be demobilized there was a fierce argument and it was decided that Alice must be the first to go. By now she was getting pretty fed up with them and, to their consternation, told them that, that being so, she would blow their cover. Frank Birch, who was appointed the official historian of signals intelligence, had the last laugh, however, as her pantomime was put on the secret list for private circulation and this is the first time it has been published. It comes from Dilly Knox's own copy. Denniston's copy was deposited with his papers at the Churchill College Archive Centre, Cambridge.

# The Carrollian Context

## by Edward Wakeling

*Alice's Adventures in Wonderland* was the invention of a mathematical lecturer at Christ Church, Oxford, Charles Lutwidge Dodgson (1832–1898), better known to us as 'Lewis Carroll,' his adopted pen-name. He was a keen wordsmith and cipher inventor, so it is no surprise that subsequent cryptographers admired his works. The original story was told to three sisters, Lorina, Alice, and Edith, daughters of Dodgson's head of college, Dean Henry George Liddell. Also with them on the occasion the tale was first told, a boat-trip from Oxford to Godstow, was Dodgson's university friend, Robinson Duckworth. The date was Friday 4 July 1862. Duckworth helped with the rowing, and entertained the children with his singing. He went on to become tutor to Queen Victoria's youngest son, Leopold, and later Canon of Westminster. The middle sister, Alice, then aged 10, begged Dodgson to write down the wonderful story he had invented for them during the long river journey; a wish he granted. The manuscript of *Alice's Adventures Under Ground* (the original title) was presented to Alice Liddell as an early Christmas gift two and a half years later in 1864, written out in his own clear hand, with illustrations of his own devising. However, plans were already well advanced to have the story published for a much wider audience, and *Alice's Adventures in Wonderland*, with 42 illustrations by John Tenniel, was published the following year in 1865. It has never been out of print since then.

There can be no doubt that Frank Birch, Dilly Knox, and the other players in this private pantomime, knew the story well. And not only the story, but also the characters and their attributes. An anonymous little girl named Alice is the principal protagonist, and the events unfold from her perspective, exactly as Alice's trip to Wonderland occurred in the book. She meets various strange characters on her journey, and engages them in conversation. From time to time she changes size – another parallel between book and parody.

The first character that Alice meets in both Dodgson's book and Frank Birch's parody is the White Rabbit. In both cases, the White Rabbit is in a hurry, and Alice chases after him, falling down a rabbit-hole in the book, and under an Admiralty arch (it seems) in the parody. The consequence is the same – a long fall into the unknown. Instead of a pile of leaves, the 20th-century Alice lands in a wire cage, her fall being down a long communications tube (with a slight pun on 'tube' – the more familiar name of the underground railway). Confusion reigns as Alice overcomes her disorientation following her descent. Questions make no sense to her. Another similarity is the great number of doors she discovers. The action turns to topsy-turvydom that borders on nonsense – typical of Dodgson's narrative in his *Alice* book. Dodgson's surreal distortion of time – time standing still at 6 o'clock – is also not quite on a regular beat in the Birch parody. Captain James's hours are 7 to 10 and 10 to 7; long enough it seems to accomplish many tasks, until we realise that this really indicates the specific time of 7 minutes to 10 and 10 minutes to 7 – very short time periods, indeed.

An oblique reference to one of Dodgson's early poems may have escaped the notice of most listeners and participants. In order for Alice to grow in size again, the Old Gentleman advises 'Harvey's Fatting Food.' In Dodgson's poem, 'Poeta Fit, Non Nascitur,' the old man suggests 'Harvey's Reading Sauce' as an adjunct to fish, or flesh, or bird – this advertisement now lost in the mists of time except perhaps for Bristol Cream. However, the ingredient had much the same effect as a piece of mushroom in the right hand. As in *Wonderland*, Alice began to grow again.

The Old Gang at the tea-party were the Hatter, the March Hare, and the Dormouse. The people in the Old Gang that Alice met this time were the founders of Room 40, established in 1914, and the precursor of Room I.D.25. They behave in a similar manner as the mad participants of the tea-party, but in this instance the Dormouse assumes a more forceful and central role. While he is busy providing material for the assembled party, one among them is acting in a very illogical manner, rather like the March Hare who offers wine to Alice on her arrival when there is none to be had, or the Hatter who asks riddles that have no answer. His objective is to 'lose things' – but this turns out to be not as illogical as it sounds because his actions employ more people whose task it is to 'find things.' Dodgson and Birch are both masters at chopped logic – nonsense that seems to make sense!

Whenever the discussion appears to be reaching a difficulty, the ploy is to 'change the subject.' The Hatter explains that they all keep moving round the table as the tea-things get used up. 'But what happens when you come to the beginning again?' Alice ventures to ask. 'Suppose we change the subject,' the March Hare interrupts. Herbert Morrah's rule is to take a shilling and find as many matches as he can. When Alice challenges the sense of this rule, he looks helpless and unhappy. Alice must change the subject. The narration is steered away from a dead-end – a typical Carrollian trick. And when all else fails, the ploy is to get the characters to recite poetry.

The text abounds in puns and wordplay and dramatic pauses – all to be found in *Alice's Adventures in Wonderland*. But many of the in-jokes are hard to fathom. When Alice says, concerning the existence of treacle-wells, 'I dare say there may be *one*,' the listeners of the tale knew well that there was a treacle-well (a healing well) at Binsey, and they may even have paused on their journey to visit it. The in-jokes in *Alice in I.D.25* have probably perished with time as a result of the long period of obscurity and secrecy imposed on the text after the first, and probably the only, performance at a private party.

Parallels between the works are easy to spot. Another example is poetry that when recited never comes out quite as expected. 'How doth the little busy bee' becomes 'How doth the little crocodile.' The verse parody in *Alice in I.D.25* is difficult to identify, but occasionally the metre sounds familiar. For example, Alice recites 'Dolores,' which adopts the rhythm of a limerick. As reciter, Alice has no control over the words that emit from her mouth – this happens in both the book and the parody.

The writing style is very similar. By way of example, consider these two extracts:

*Alice's Adventures in Wonderland*

The Gryphon lifted up both its paws in surprise. 'Never heard of uglifying!' it exclaimed. 'You know what to beautify is, I suppose?'

'Yes,' said Alice doubtfully: 'it means – to – make – anything – prettier.'

*Alice in I.D.25*

'But what kind of a tree?' asked Alice, who had never seen one like it before.

'It's a Grumbling Willow,' he replied.

'I don't believe there is such a thing,' Alice protested. 'At least, I never heard of one.'

'Well, you've heard of a Weeping Willow?'

'Oh, yes.'

'Well, this is a Grumbling Willow.'

Here's another example for comparison:

*Alice in I.D.25*

'But where is the Directional room?' she inquired, bewildered.

'Why, there of course,' howled the Waterflap, pointing to a door.

'How could I possibly know that!' Alice exclaimed, angered by his rudeness.

'Silly girl,' it hissed. 'Why, it's called the Directional room because it's in that direction,' and it pushed her roughly through the doorway.

*Alice's Adventures in Wonderland*
'The master was an old Turtle – we used to call him Tortoise –'
'Why did you call him Tortoise, if he wasn't one?' Alice asked.
'We called him Tortoise because he taught us,' said the Mock Turtle angrily. 'Really you are very dull!'

The similarities are obvious. Other characters from the *Alice* books make an appearance in *Alice in I.D.25*, such as the argumentative Humpty Dumpty from *Looking-Glass* and the wise Dodo from *Wonderland*. And the language used by the characters is similar; from 'mouse-traps, and the moon, and memory, and muchness' to 'beer – or books – or buffaloes.' There's a pedantic Mouse, and Alice even recognises the Mad Hatter (although he is only known as the Hatter in *Wonderland*), from her earlier 19th-century experiences. But he has changed – smaller and less significant, childish and inept – allusions lost on us today.

Portmanteau words (the combination of two well-known words into a new word, probably first invented by Dodgson) also make an appearance, such as 'transubstantiation.'

The story ends in similar mode. Alice gains her confidence and accuses them all of being no more than a pack of cards, or she threatens to tell the truth and it's all over – they are a lot of c-creatures! *Alice in I.D.25* is clever in the Carrollian tradition, humorous and witty like the immortal book, and with depths of meaning that we may never fully unravel.

# Alice in I.D. 25

Alice was walking down Whitehall one day, after breakfast at the 'Ship,' when suddenly from one of the windows above there fluttered a sheet of paper which came planing down at her feet. She picked it up while her nurse was looking the other way and saw that there was writing on it, but when she came to read it she could not make out a word of sense.

This is what it said:

Ballybunion – Short begins – ud – sn – dd – um – um – v.v.v. – depresses key – fierce x's and wipers.

As soon as she began to read, a curious feeling came over her. She seemed to grow smaller and smaller and the people in the street began to fade away. She was just about to let the paper go when the White Rabbit appeared, obviously very important and in a great hurry. He was dressed in his Sunday best – spats, spectacles, and a little black coat, and he kept doing up and undoing its buttons with nervousness.

'Dear me, dear me,' Alice heard him say as he passed her, 'it's past ten. I shall be late for the DIND. I *must* be there when he comes round. I *always* am,' and with that he bustled out of earshot.

Before she knew what she was doing, Alice found herself running after him, and she was just beginning to catch up when he turned sharply to the right, and disappeared under an arch.

'Really, it's most provoking,' panted Alice when she came up. 'I wonder *which* arch he used; there seem to be so many. Yes – no – yes. I think it was this one. Anyway, I'll try.' And repeating to herself for some reason, 'Ballybunion – Short begins,' &c., she dived under the nearest arch. As she did so the ground gave way under her feet, and she found herself falling, falling, falling down a deep, deep well. Only it wasn't an ordinary kind of well, because it was not straight but turned and twisted; and at the turnings Alice only just managed to squeeze past.

'After all, it may be only the Metropolitan or the Tube,' thought Alice, a well-informed child for her age, to reassure herself. 'I wonder how far and how fast I am falling. Perhaps I ought to count.' So she started counting slowly: 'One – two – three – four,' and so on, until, just when she got to 'forty,' something opened with a chop below her, and she fell into daylight onto something rather hard and uncomfortable.

She sat up and took notice. She appeared to be in a sort of cage of golden wire, through which she could see into an immense room where there were many huge creatures. But Alice remembered that she herself had shrunk and supposed that they were all really only a normal size, except perhaps for one *quite* little man seated at a desk in the far corner by the window. All the other creatures in the room – and there were a great many – were fast asleep. Now while Alice was taking stock she heard a noise above her, and a large heavy object like a dumb-bell fell into the basket beside her.

'Lucky it didn't fall on me,' thought she, and looked for a means of escape. The cage she found had no top to it, and she was about to climb up the side when she was seized from above by an enormous hand and put down on a table.

'Good heavens,' said a voice, 'what's this? – How did *you* get here?'

'Please I fell down,' replied Alice, rather breathlessly, 'but I'm not hurt – at least not much,' she added as she rubbed her elbows, 'though I did get rather badly jammed at the corners.'

'So I see,' said the voice, and she was lifted up again and inspected closely.

'What's your time-group?' it went on.

'I beg your pardon!' said Alice politely, but much puzzled.

'What's your time-group? You must have a time-group.'

'I – I – I am afraid I haven't got one,' answered Alice, feeling unaccountably rather ashamed of herself.

'Well, if you haven't got a time-group, you must be either N.S.L. or Baltic. If you are Baltic I must give you to the Watch, but if –' But he never finished the sentence, for at the word 'Baltic' all the creatures in the room, who had been fast asleep, suddenly put up their heads and howled in chorus: 'We *don't* do Baltic. We *won't* do Baltic. We never *have* done Baltic. It's a tradition.' Whereupon they dropped their heads upon their arms and went to sleep again.

'Very well,' said the creature, picking Alice up again, 'you'd better go with N.S.L.,' and he dropped her rather roughly on to a heap of papers in a big tin, and from time to time threw others on top of her, until she was completely buried.

Alice was so frightened that she lay quite still where she had fallen. Presently she fell asleep and was only woken up by hearing a clock strike one. She sat up and climbed to the top of the pile of papers. The room was empty. After making quite sure, she scrambled out of the tin, dropped to the floor, and ran to a door. It wouldn't open. There were a great many other doors, but they all seemed to lead to other rooms. At last, just as she was going to sit down and cry, she found one that was marked, 'This door must be kept shut.' It was wide open and she hurried through it. As a matter of fact, she need not have been in such a hurry, because all the creatures had gone to lunch and would not be back till four.

Alice now found herself in a passage. She walked along it and turned corners until she was thoroughly lost, and at last came back to where she had started from. But the door was now shut, and there was a notice on it which read: 'Engaged. Please ring the bell.'

'Perhaps I had better inquire the way out,' thought Alice, and looked for the bell, but there wasn't one. 'What funny people,' she added, and then saw another placard on the door which said: 'Enquire Room 48.'

Alice started to look for Room 48. Room 49 was quite close, but none of the other numbers appeared to have anything to do with each other. At last, just as she turned the corner of a narrow dark passage, she ran into a large creature, who looked something between a Labour Member and Sir Francis Drake. He kept on turning out his pockets and poking into the dark corners.

'Mornin', Miss,' said this gentleman in a voice husky, – with emotion Alice thought. ''Ave you seen a bed anywhere?'

'No,' replied Alice, 'I haven't.'

'I've *lost* a bed,' he went on. 'There was two in 47 and one in –' and so he went on, ticking them off on his fingers. 'That makes 12,' he summed up, 'and there were only eleven this morning. I shouldn't be surprised if it weren't that hungry creature in 53. Very careless 'e is. Tried to bathe in it I *daresay*, and swallowed it.'

Alice thought all this great nonsense and was wondering what she ought to do next, when the Old Gentleman suddenly remembered her presence and said: 'What can I do for you, Miss?'

'I – I was following the White Rabbit, as I wanted to see the DIND,' she replied, 'but I got lost.'

'Well,' said he, 'you ought by rights to see Captain James, I suppose; but he won't be here yet awhile. His hours are 7 to 10 and 10 to 7.'

Alice thought these very long hours indeed and couldn't see why Captain James wasn't there since it must be about 2 p.m., but she did not want to start an argument, and besides the old man had quite forgotten her again and was muttering to himself, as he scratched his head.

'Nice chap, Captain James. Knows 'is place. Mind you, I 'ave known owners as couldn't leave you alone, but 'e ain't there more'n 'e's wanted. 'E leaves it to me.' Then he saw Alice again and resumed. 'Very well, my dear. In the absence of Captain James it's my place to show you round. But –' he added doubtfully – 'you're a bit small as you are.'

'Yes,' agreed Alice, 'I've been badly jammed – I mean, I have shrunk.'

'That won't matter. A little bit of Harvey's Fatting Food will put you to rights. I'll go and fetch some from 52.'

Alice employed the time while she was waiting in looking about her. To one side was a door on which was written: 'The Mansion House' and underneath it: 'This is the Lord Mayor's Show.'

On the door facing her was a notice which Alice could just read by standing on tiptoe. It ran:

THE OLD GANG.
FOUNDED 1914.
THE CREDIT SYSTEM.

At this moment, back came the Old Gentleman.

"'Ere, Missy, you take a nibble at this,' and he pressed into her hand a little white tabloid. 'Just like a formamint,' thought Alice, so she took a bite. Almost before she could swallow, she began to grow and grow quite alarmingly.

'That's enough,' came a warning. 'You don't want to overdo it. I remember a professor what nearly did 'imself in by eatin' two of 'em,' and he made Alice give back what was left. She was now her usual size and felt much better in consequence.

'What's the Old Gang?' she asked.

'Oh, they're very important people,' said her guide. 'Come in and have a look at them,' and he opened the door and pushed Alice into the room.

At one end there was a row of tables at which a number of creatures were seated huddled together. In the middle Alice recognized the Dormouse, very quiet and apparently asleep. Only he was much larger than he used to be and wore a coronet. On either side of him clustered a number of other creatures, and looking over his shoulder was the White Rabbit.

'How very uncomfortable it must be to be squashed together like that,' thought Alice, and aloud she said: 'Why don't they sit further apart?'

'Wait and see,' whispered the Old Gentleman solemnly.

Alice waited and saw that every now and then the Dormouse woke up and wrote something down on a bit of paper. Whenever he did so, there was a general scramble and whoever managed to get the paper shouted: 'I have got out the chi,' or 'I have got out the key,' or something *like* that.

Alice thought this somehow very unfair, though she could not quite understand what it was all about.

'What are they doing?' she asked the Old Gentleman.

'They're researching.'

'But what for?'

'For credit, of course,' he answered.

'And do they find it?'

'Well, they generally get *given* it,' he admitted.

'And if we're not given it,' suddenly yelled the White Rabbit defiantly, 'we jolly well go and *take* it.'

At this there were cries of 'Hear, hear' and general applause, which only ceased when a fresh scramble started for a piece of paper on which the Dormouse had scribbled something.

Alice was still watching them when her guide pointed her out a slim, well-groomed creature with a black moustache who was seated all alone in the opposite corner of the room. He seemed to be very busy and conscientious, but Alice noticed that every now and then, when he thought no one was looking, he would take a paper out of one file and put it in another, or sidle it into a drawer, or even throw it into the fire.

'Who is he?' asked Alice.

'He's the P.P.S.,' whispered the guide.

'What's that?' she inquired.

'The Perfect Public Servant,' he explained.

'But what's he *doing*?' she insisted.

'He's *losing* things.'

'But why?'

'Well, if somebody didn't *lose* things, there'd be no use having people to find them, and a lot of people would be thrown out of work.

After all,' he added, seeing that Alice was still puzzled, 'it's better to lose your papers than your job.'

Alice was about to ask a lot more questions, when her attention was diverted by a scuffle at the other end of the room. The animals were pushing and dragging the Dormouse into the passage. Someone had tied a label round his neck marked 'To Paris,' and they were all shouting, 'Send him away, turn him out.'

'What's the matter?' asked Alice, who felt sorry for the poor creature. Whereupon they all screamed: 'He does his own work and minds his own business. We don't want *that* sort of thing here,' and pushed him out of the room.

'But what will they do now he's gone?' Alice asked the Old Gentleman.

'Oh, *that's* all right,' he replied. 'They've always got the other one,' and he pointed to a very quiet creature in a bowler hat and paymaster's uniform who was going on with his work as if nothing had happened.

Alice thought she ought to go and comfort the Dormouse, so she said: 'I think I will run after him, if you don't mind.'

'That's right, Miss,' said her friend, while a curious glint came into his eyes, 'I'll just step out for a minute to see a man about a dog. Shan't be long;' and he hurried off, drawing the back of his hand succulently across his mouth.

When Alice reached the passage she saw a figure retreating in the distance. 'There's the Dormouse,' she murmured and ran after him. 'I'm so sorry,' she began as she caught him up, 'I –.'

But to her surprise, when the creature turned round, it wasn't the Dormouse at all, but a dark, dreamy creature with soft eyes and a white underlip where a moustache had once nestled. He carried a box of matches in one hand and a lyre in the other. His pockets were stuffed with papers, and one which stuck out a long way was marked 'Weather Chart.'

Alice felt very shy at having spoken to a perfect stranger.

'I beg your pardon,' she apologized; 'I thought –.'

'Certainly not, certainly not,' said the creature generously. 'I have just come back from Rome, so we have never met, though no doubt you have heard of me. Allow me to introduce myself,' and he produced a visiting card which he handed to Alice. On it was written in a fair round hand:

*Herbert Arthur Morrah, Esq.*

**Authors' Club.**                    **War Staff (Adty.)**

'Yes,' he went on, 'but that's not all. There's a lot more – oh, yes, a lot. It's all in "Who's Who." Do you know "Who's Who"?'

'I'm afraid I don't,' Alice confessed.

'Oh, you should, you should. It's a great book – I wrote part of it,' he added proudly.

'Really!' said Alice politely.

'Well, in "Who's Who,"' he whispered, leaning towards her – 'in "Who's Who," *I'm Me*.' And he nodded wisely and watched the effect of his revelation.

Alice didn't quite understand, but he didn't seem to expect her to say anything, so she was silent.

'Have a match,' he said suddenly, holding one out to her.

'Thanks very much,' she replied, taking it.

'That'll be a shilling,' and he smiled benignantly as he held out his hand. Now Alice knew that matches were scarce, but she couldn't help protesting all the same.

'Isn't that rather expensive?' she inquired.

'Not at all.' He shook his head. 'That's the rule. Everybody gives me a shilling, and I find as many matches as I can.'

'I think it's a very *silly* rule,' said Alice, feeling rather annoyed.

'But I *have* to do it. I *have* to!' he exclaimed, rolling his eyes and waving his arms. 'It's my *War* Work.'

He looked so helpless and unhappy that Alice hastened to change the subject.

'Won't you recite something you have written, please?' she asked.

'Well, if you *insist*,' he cried, brightening. 'There is a little thing I was writing when I was last on Watch. That's the best time, you know,' he added confidentially.

'I see,' said Alice, though she didn't really. 'How does it go?'

'It *comes*,' he corrected, 'like this,' and he began to recite in a melancholy voice:

Then the Soldier gave
A parting wave
And murmured 'Damn' and 'Begorrah,'
But for language bad
The Irish lad
Found more than his match in Morrah.

'Of course you understand the allusions, *don't* you,' he broke off. 'There's the point about the "match," for instance. Ha! Ha! Ha!' and he laughed a sad little laugh that became ashamed of itself and ended in a sigh. 'The Soldier,' he went on gently, 'is Fraser. You know, he has a conspiracy against me, so I don't mind being *terribly* rude about *him*.'

Alice thought so mild a creature could never be rude, but she didn't say anything, because he resumed the poem at once:

But Grey sat on the quarter-deck
And never an oath swore he,
What time the good ship 'President'
Went sailing forth to sea.

'Is there any more?' asked Alice, seeing that he had stopped.

'Of course there is,' he complained, 'but there must be a pause between the verses,' and after a minute or two he went on:

> Lord Herschall was dumb,
> For seas of rum
> Had left him but half alive.
> Our Commanders split
> A bottle of it
> And James an infinitive.
> But Grey he sat on the quarter-deck
> And never a glass quaffed he,
> What time the good ship 'President'
> Went sailing forth to sea.

'Thank you very much,' said Alice, when she was quite sure he had finished.

'Of course,' the creature explained languidly, 'that's a *long* poem. Mostly I write short ones and I call them "Epigrams." Would you like to hear one?'

'Yes, please,' she replied, not feeling quite certain what an epigram was.

'Well,' he said, as he drew a bunch of papers from his pocket, 'here is one.'

'It looks very long,' thought Alice, seeing the size of the bunch.

'You see,' he went on, 'I always make a lot of copies, in case I don't publish. Sometimes I publish them, but more often I just leave them about – under the blotting-paper or in one of the tins,' and with that he began to intone.

EPIGRAM.

> Me fate would waft had I my wish
> Where rules with Dagon's rod
> Our Sailor Padre, ½ a fish
> And ½ a god.

'Beautiful, beautiful,' he murmured wistfully, after a pause. Then he turned suddenly to Alice and said: 'Do you know any poetry?'

'Ye-e-e-s,' she acknowledged doubtfully. 'Of course, I have to learn things by heart.'

'And what do you know by heart?'

'Well, there's "Dolores,"' she replied. 'I've just learned that.'

'"Dolores"? "Dolores"?' he sighed. 'How dreadfully advanced. Never mind, begin, child, begin.'

Alice was a little uncertain whether she knew it perfectly, but began at once:

> There were forty who laughed at the Prophet,
> But your faults which are forty-four score,
> Though all forty should aid us to scoff, it
> Would take us a fortnight or more;
> And then it would leave without story
> The queer little follies of One
> Who sits by the window in glory,
> Our Figure of Fun.

Alice felt somehow that something had gone wrong, but she went on bravely:

> A soldier in Room 51
> Was as long and as thin as a gun.
> He perpetually paid his
> Attention to ladies, –
> He worshipped them every one.

By this time Alice realized that something had happened to the words since she learnt them, but they came so easily to her lips, that it hardly needed the encouragement of the poet, who kept murmuring dreamily, 'Go on, go on,' to make her continue:

A subtle, peculiar leaven
Are the angels of Room 47.
They garner in store
What they sowed not before,
For of such is the Kingdom of Heaven.

The sailor in Room 53
Has never, it's true, been to sea.
But though not in a boat,
He has yet served afloat –
In a bath at the Admiralty.

It is commonly thought we derive
Great blessings from Room 45.
Our courtly Lord Mayor,
By his policy there,
Has rescued the Empire alive.

There were four fair ladies in 40
Whose manners were distant and haughty.
Cried one, dressed in patchwork,
'We won't do this Watchwork!'
    – How naughty! –

A pilot in Room 49
Devotes unto questions divine
What time he can spare
From Wilson's hot air, –
Far be his conclusions from mine.

A fellow in Room 52
Has a nose like a nat'ralized Jew.
His colleagues shout: '*Crikey!*

There goes little Ikey,' –
But, of course, it is wholly untrue.


The Captain in Room 54
Employs men and girls by the score.
But organisation
Leaves no occupation
For the Captain himself any more.


Our minds are unable to fix
The uses of Room 56.
Yet *they* show no compunction
Concerning their function;
No scruple of conscience pricks.


The Ruler of Room 55
Is able at once to contrive
Ten different tasks,
And like Oliver asks
'For more. May *she* prosper and thrive.'


Alice felt as if she had been wound up and might go on for ever like that. But at this minute the creature interrupted by asking: 'And who is *she*, pray?'

'Why, Auntie, of course,' Alice replied, though she couldn't think why.

'Hm,' said the creature. 'She sounds almost as bad as the White Rabbit.'

'Yes, I suppose so,' muttered Alice, '– not at all the sort of Ruler I should like in my Home.'

'Rule in your Home? *Home* Rule? Did I hear you say *Home* Rule?' shouted the creature violently, while an extraordinary change came over him. 'Yes, you did say Home Rule. That's it! I heard you! Home Rule!' and his voice grew louder and louder and his eyes rolled and he beat his hands together and waved his arms and looked so fierce and dangerous, that Alice began to feel quite frightened.

At the same moment a shadow covered them and, looking upwards, Alice saw a huge bird with webbed feet and great floppy wings fly over them both.

'KR, KR, KR,' it croaked as it alighted and disappeared through a doorway. But the poet paid no attention. He only got more and more wild, till Alice started to run in the direction where she had last seen the bird, to ask it for protection, but when she had gone a little way she couldn't make up her mind which room he had entered.

The Waterflap.

While she was still hesitating, up came the Old Gentleman. Alice was very glad to see him.

'Oh dear, oh dear,' she explained, 'I've just left a creature in a fit and I hoped –'

'Never mind him,' interrupted her friend. ''E's quite 'armless really, only just a little bit –,' but instead of finishing his sentence, he tapped his forehead knowingly and winked. 'Come and see the Waterflap. It's this minute arrived,' he went on, dragging her after him to see the great bird.

'I hope you met your friend all right,' said Alice politely, as they went along.

He looked at her suspiciously for a moment before he replied rather gruffly, 'Yes, thank you, I did.' But his eyes were so moist and his voice so husky that Alice felt quite sorry for him.

'It must have been a very *great* friend, and the parting must have been *dreadfully* sad,' she thought.

She was ushered into a small room composed chiefly of doors and windows. The first thing she noticed was the Waterflap. It was lying in a chair exhausted after its flight.

'SSD, SSd, Ssd, ssd,' it puffed, just like a steam-engine, thought Alice, as she examined it. At first sight it seemed more like a vulture or a griffin, but at last she decided it must be an owl, because its eyes were hooded.

In the further corner at a table another creature was seated writing, while beside him stood what Alice took to be a very gnarled log. It swayed to and fro, and groaned as it did so.

'What's that?' she asked, pointing to it.

'That's a tree,' said the Old Gentleman, 'and a very stout tree, too.'

'But what kind of a tree?' asked Alice, who had never seen one like it before.

'It's a Grumbling Willow,' he replied.

'I don't believe there is such a thing,' Alice protested. 'At least, I never heard of one.'

'Well, you've heard of a Weeping Willow?'

'Oh, yes.'

'Well, this is a Grumbling Willow.'

Alice had to own that if there was a Weeping Willow there might just as well be a Grumbling one, so she gave up the argument.

'But who is that creature writing in the book?' she went on after a pause.

'Oh, that's the Chief Clerk,' he replied.

Alice drew close to him, and, looking over his shoulder, saw that he was copying things off pieces of paper into a book.

'Why,' she exclaimed, suddenly remembering, 'you're doing exactly the same thing as the creature I saw sitting at the tube.'

'Ah!' drawled the Chief Clerk knowingly, 'that's just it.'

'Just what?' asked Alice.

'What you said,' he replied. 'You see,' he went on, perceiving Alice's puzzled expression, 'you can't have too many people doing the same thing. One of them is *bound* to do it right.'

'They *all* do it wrong,' groaned the Tree. '*Always. Everywhere*,' and he snapped his twigs. However, the Chief Clerk paid no attention, but went on writing.

Alice now noticed that the Waterflap, having recovered its breath, had written out things on bits of paper marked 'Notice,' and had pinned them up on the wall. One read: 'When in doubt send for the DIND,' and another: 'Not more than two typewriters are to be used at once;' and so on. It was now busy biting its pen in the middle of a longer composition.

'What are you writing?' she ventured to ask.

'An Appreciation,' it croaked.

'Why is it called that?' she inquired.

'Because the Grumbling Willow appreciates it,' replied the Waterflap. Alice heard the Tree mumble something that did not *sound* complimentary, but before she could ask him to repeat it, a creature appeared from next door with a sheet of paper.

'*Give* it me! Give it *me*!' shrieked the Waterflap, snatching it, and he read out in a voice which grew more and more excited: 'Zurübung. Bitte Signal wiederholen. Besser geben.'

'KR, KR, KR,' it cawed when it had finished, and, jumping up, hopped about the room, flapping its wings. 'It's a new cypher! The Fleet's out!' And it rushed to a table on which a chart was pinned, seized hold of all the flags on the right-hand side and plunked them into the middle of the chart. 'Send for Captain James,' it yelled, as it upset the tables and knocked the other creatures on to the floor. 'Send for the DIND. Send for the King! Fire! Fire!! Fire!!!' Then it rushed to the window, threw it open and flung all the typewriters into the yard.

'Can I do anything?' Alice suggested timidly, thinking that something dreadful must have happened.

The Waterflap jumped as if it had been shot. 'What are *you* doing here?' it snapped. 'Take this at once into the Directional room,' and it thrust the paper which had caused all the fuss into her hands.

'But where *is* the Directional room?' she inquired, bewildered.

'Why, there of course,' howled the Waterflap, pointing to a door.

'How could I possibly know that!' Alice exclaimed, angered by his rudeness.

'Silly girl,' it hissed. 'Why, it's *called* the Directional room because it's in that *direction*,' and it pushed her roughly through the doorway.

Alice found herself in a large room with a high table in the middle of it. On the farther side of the table were grouped a number of creatures with their heads together, some of them exactly talking, but some whispering and the rest shouting.

'What are you doing?' asked Alice as soon she could make herself heard.

'We're plotting,' whispered a Billykins with a red fringe to his bald head. Alice was much impressed. 'I believe this is *very* important,' she said, handing him the piece of paper in her hand. He looked at it casually for nearly a second, then threw it into the waste-paper basket. Alice waited for him to say something, but he merely rejoined the others, and they all began playing a game with little pieces of string with weighted ends, a kind of bumble-puppy, Alice thought. She went on watching them for a time, but as they did not ask her to join in, her attention began to wander.

There was an armchair by the fire and a great round thing lying in it. She went towards it, and as she drew nearer, saw that it had eyes and a nose and a mouth, just like a human being.

'Why, it's Humpty Dumpty!' she exclaimed. 'Fancy meeting you here,' she went on, holding out her hand.

'Ah,' he said dolefully as he took it, 'I'm not the creature I was – not since the rationing came in.'

'You don't look any different,' Alice consoled him.

'Ah,' he sighed, 'you shouldn't judge by appearances; it's the feeling inside that matters. Not but what,' he added, as he succeeded at last in buttoning his coat, 'it is certainly easier to make both ends meet.'

'But what have you been doing since I saw you last?' Alice inquired.

'Well, for one thing,' said Humpty Dumpty, 'I've just come back from the Fleet.'

'Really?' exclaimed Alice, very much surprised, 'and what were you doing there?'

'They sent for me,' he cried proudly, 'to do what neither Jellicoe nor Beatty could do!' And he began to roll in his chair like an egg in a cup.

'What was that?' she asked.

'To sink the German Fleet,' he shouted.

'And did you do it?'

'Did I do it?' he puffed, rolling so heavily that Alice thought he would fall out of the chair. 'Of course I did. I only had to *push* the T.B.D.s. I had to put one foot on the cruisers and both on the battleships – all except the "BADEN." I *jumped* on her, and she sank slowly underneath me.'

'I wonder you didn't sink too,' laughed Alice, who didn't know whether to believe him or not.

'I *can't* sink,' he replied in an injured tone. 'I float.'

'Why do you float?' she asked.

'You mean *what* do I float,' he corrected.

'No, I mean *why* do you float,' she repeated.

'*What*,' he insisted crossly.

'No, *why*.'

'What.'

'Why.'

'What.'

And so they went on. 'Oh, very well,' said Alice at last, 'it doesn't matter. What do you float then?'

'Why, *loans*, of course.'

Alice was by this time quite sure that something was wrong with him, and now she noticed that the egg was cracked at the top. 'Addled, as I thought,' she said to herself.

'Further,' he resumed bombastically, 'I have established a great reputation for tact.'

'Have you?' said Alice in a soothing tone.

'I have. I call it pouring oil on troubled waters.'

'What sort of oil?' she asked, more to humour him than for any other reason.

'Persian oil, you know,' he answered self-consciously, 'and Standard oil – any oil in fact, except Shell. Very successful it was, too. You ask Captain James,' and he subsided against the back of the chair, jerking his thumb over his shoulder.

Alice, looking in that direction, saw an open doorway leading to another room. She went to the entrance and saw a much more comfortable apartment than she had yet met with. It was quite empty except for a little Lady Mouse dressed in a sailor suit, who was sitting with her back to Alice near the door and writing things at the bottom of sheets of paper.

'When will Captain James be in?' asked Alice politely.

'They *all* ask that,' the Mouse replied resignedly. 'He won't be in for an hour or two. His hours are 7 to 10 and 10 to 7,' and she went on writing.

'Do you mind my asking,' ventured Alice after a pause, 'what it is you are doing?'

'I'm forging signatures,' said the Mouse mildly.

'Do you do much of that?' asked Alice, surprised.

'All day long,' sighed the Mouse.

'And why do you underline everything like that,' Alice went on, peeping over her shoulder.

'One must draw the line somewhere,' the Mouse replied with dignity. With that she went back to her work, paying no attention to Alice but muttering to herself things that sounded like 'First-class return at half the ordinary single fare.' Alice was beginning to feel rather lonely, when up came the Old Gentleman.

'What, still here, missy!' he exclaimed. 'You must hurry up and visit the rest of the out-patients, or you'll be late for the DIND in Room 40.' So saying, he led Alice out of the room into a little, dark cul-de-sac. On the door opposite was a placard marked

MIXED BATHING.

'I'll just hand you over to Dilly the Dodo,' said the guide hoarsely, 'and then you won't want me any more, so I think I'll step out and see a man about a dog.'

'What, *another* friend?' ejaculated Alice.

'Yes, another one,' he replied shortly.

Alice was just wondering if he had a great many friends and if they *all* had dogs, when he opened the door, pushed Alice inside and, with a shout of 'Tea ready, Gentlemen, please,' disappeared, slamming the door behind her.

The room was a *very* tiny one, 'no bigger than a bathing machine' Alice thought, and the table in the middle was so big that you could only just squeeze between it and the wall. Alice had plenty of time to take everything in because none of the creatures there took any notice of her. They were all scowling very hard at the table in front of them.

'Please can you tell me which is Dilly the Dodo!' Alice inquired politely after a minute or two.

'I am,' replied one of the creatures jumping up. Alice thought he was the queerest bird she had ever seen. He was so long and lean, and he had outgrown his clothes, and his face was like a pang of hunger.

'I was told to come to you,' said Alice, rather disconcerted.

'You must ask the Secretary, ask the Secretary,' he answered with a wave of the paw. 'It is unconstitutional to approach me except through the Secretary,' and he sat down again.

Alice hesitated for a few seconds, but thought she would try again. 'Isn't it rather a *small* room?' she began.

'Not really,' said the Dodo huffily; 'not *really* a small room. It's just the right size, when you come to think. Of course, you know the Greek definition of the ideal room?'

'I'm afraid I don't,' Alice apologized.

'The ideal room is such,' the Dodo quoted, 'that a man standing in the centre can touch floor, ceiling, and all four walls.'

'Really,' said Alice, at a loss for anything better to say. Then she went on. 'But you *can't* stand in the middle of *this* room, because of the table.'

'I don't see the difficulty,' he snapped.

Alice thought the creature very hard to please, but she hastened to change the conversation.

'So you are very fond of Greek?' she inquired.

'Greek or Latin, Latin or Greek,' he replied. 'I love all the Classics. That's why I brought my brother here. He's a Roman, you know.'

Alice couldn't see how a Dodo could have a Roman brother, but, before she could ask for an explanation, he went on more kindly.

'Perhaps you would like to see some of my work,' and he handed her a sheet of very dirty paper on which a spider with inky feet appeared to have been crawling.

'It looks very clever,' Alice suggested politely, 'but I'm afraid it's all Greek to me.'

'That's why I like it so much,' the Dodo smiled. 'Let me explain it to you. It's three-letter stuff, you see, so we have one person for each letter.'

'But there are four of you,' counted Alice.

'You know the rule, don't you?' he said pityingly. 'One for each letter and one for the pot.'

Alice thought she had never heard such nonsense, but just at this moment she caught sight of a bath at one end of the room.

'Why, I thought it was a bathing-machine,' she exclaimed, 'but it's got a bath in it.'

'My idea,' smiled the Dodo self-consciously; 'you see, with an ordinary bathing-machine, you have to leave it to bathe. But in this one you can bathe without leaving it. – Not that we ever do,' he went on vaguely, 'but it's very useful to put things in.'

'What sort of things?' asked Alice.

'Oh, anything that comes along,' he cried impatiently; 'beer – or books – or buffaloes.'

'But a buffalo couldn't get into it,' protested Alice.

He considered this a minute.

'It might,' he said at last, gently, 'if you cut it up. Then you know,' he went on wisely, 'there are an awful lot of rats about here.'

'I don't see what that's got to do with it,' said Alice, feeling rather dazed.

'Well, you see, one of them might get into the bath, and then you could turn on the tap and drown it. It's best to be prepared, you know, because you *never* know. – There might be one there now,' he added nervously and began fumbling in his pockets.

'What's the matter?' asked Alice.

'I've lost my spectacles,' cried the Dodo angrily, as he turned up the chairs and table.

'Where *are* my spectacles?' and he glared angrily at the Secretary.

'I expect they are in *that*,' jerked the Secretary, pointing to a tobacco-pouch on the table.

'Of course, of course,' cried the Dodo foolishly. He opened the pouch and there, sure enough, were the spectacles.

Alice could not help asking the strange creature why he kept his glasses in a tobacco-pouch.

'A little idea of mine,' he smirked. 'Rather ingenious, don't you think? You see, by this means, when I find my spectacles I remember my tobacco.'

'But where is it?' asked Alice, puzzled.

'Well, if the spectacles are in the tobacco-pouch, the tobacco must be in the spectacle-case. It follows, you know, by logic,' and with that he took his spectacle-case from his pocket and opened it. Inside was *not* tobacco at all, but a long and thin ham sandwich.

Alice was about to ask for an explanation when the Dodo went on triumphantly.

'You see how it works? Now *this* serves to remind me that I am hungry.'

Poor Alice was now completely bewildered, but she managed to ask: 'Can't you remember when you are hungry?'

'I'm always hungry,' he gobbled, 'but I can't always remember it. Being hungry,' he went on with his mouth full, 'is like being in debt. You always are, but you sometimes need to be reminded of it. That's why I work at night. You see, you get more meals that way. The night Watch,' he murmured dreamily, 'is very generous. And that reminds me,' he suddenly shouted, 'it's tea-time. Come on!' and seizing Alice by the hand he ran with her out of the room.

Down an incline and across a passage they rushed, into a large room in which several creatures were seated opposite each other, two to each table and apparently engaged in pushing the tables into each other.

'Who are these?' panted Alice, as the Dodo swept her towards a door marked

BIG BEN'S DEN.

'People of no importance,' cried the Dodo haughtily, 'but I'll introduce you if you like. You see those two,' he went on, pointing to two small creatures, crouching hopelessly among a mass of paper and trying to keep their heads above the surface. 'That's the Hanley-Page combination. You've *heard* of them probably. The aeroplane experts, you know. Over in the far corner the creature with the eyebrows is Peter Pan, and that's his Golliwog opposite.'

At this moment a timid little creature in spectacles approached from another part of the room.

'Can you lend me a few pennies?' it whispered slyly to Alice, 'it's for the bus, you know.'

Alice felt in her coat pocket and produced a three-penny bit.

'Thank you so much,' it blushed its acknowledgement and wandered away blinking and muttering to itself: 'Quite a long ride, on a white bus.' But before Alice could hear any more, she was whisked through the little door.

A huge creature inside was conducting an orchestra of typewriters with the much-bitten end of a pencil as they entered, but as soon as the creature saw them she shouted 'Tea' in an authoritative voice, whereupon the typewriting creatures all ran out of the room and an entirely different lot of animals took their places. Alice couldn't make out why this was so, but as she was only a guest she didn't like to say anything.

'This is Big Ben,' said the Dodo in a respectful tone by way of introduction.

'Why do they call her that?' Alice whispered while Big Ben was pouring out the tea.

'Because she's so striking, of course,' replied the Dodo admiringly. 'Don't you think she is?'

Before Alice could answer there came a timid tap at the door.

'Come in,' shouted Big Ben.

The door opened and in tottered the Mad Hatter. He looked much smaller and more insignificant than when Alice had last seen him, and he was staggering along with an enormous tin labelled 'Tobacco' in his arms.

'Yes, you may come in now,' Big Ben went on, glaring at him. 'Oh dear, was there ever such a nuisance?' she cried suddenly as the Mad Hatter in his nervousness tripped over the kettle which was lying on the hearth and fell sprawling on the floor, while the tobacco tin rolled away under a table.

'Get up, get up, you little beast,' scolded Big Ben, as she picked him up and shook him. 'Now, get into your chair,' and with that she tied a bib round his neck and pushed him into the corner.

'Please may I have my tea?' the Mad Hatter pleaded after a pause.

'Here you are,' answered Big Ben, handing him a huge mug and a piece of stale bread.

Alice couldn't help laughing at the Hatter's awkwardness. The mug was so big that, whenever he tried to drink out of it, he had to stand on tiptoe and bend the whole of his body over it until his head had completely disappeared. Very dangerous, thought Alice, and she was standing by to render assistance if necessary, when a voice thundered in her ear.

'*Don't* you?' it cried.

'I'm very sorry,' said Alice, turning to find Big Ben towering above her, 'I didn't quite hear what you said.'

'Don't you think I ought to have a joy-ride? All the creatures have been. Why, they even let *that* go to Harwich,' and she pointed a withering finger at the Hatter. 'I call it a beastly swizzle. I shan't do any more work.'

'Big Ben strikes again,' muttered a voice thickly from the mug.

'Have some more cake,' suggested Big Ben, disregarding the interruption, and she pushed a plateful of fragments towards Alice. 'We always ask people in,' she confided, 'when there's a lot of old stuff to be eaten up.'

Alice was thinking how she could refuse without giving offence, when the Dodo, who had been stuffing silently all this time, suddenly jumped up and doddered past her, crying: 'I must go to Room 40 and find fault with things. Come along.' Alice started after him, but, hearing a scream paused in the doorway and, looking over her shoulder, saw that the Mad Hatter had fallen into his mug and was spluttering in the tea while Big Ben fished for him leisurely with a hat-pin.

When Alice reached the passage, the Dodo was already a long way off. She was about to break into a run when she heard sobs behind her.

Turning she saw the Hatter stumbling along, blinded by his tears and the tea which was streaming from him.

'It's a great shame,' he slobbered as he came up. 'It's *my* room really, you know, only she won't let me stay in it.'

Alice murmured something sympathetic, but the only result was a new outburst of weeping.

'You know,' he whimpered, 'I was quite pink and chubby when I first came here, but she's driven me to this. She bullies me,' he screamed. 'She's – she's – she's a Vampire!' and with a parting cry of 'That's Room 40,' he staggered blubbering away.

Alice recognized the room as soon as she entered. There was the tube, and there was the Watch fast asleep, and there was the Little Man in the corner by the window. As soon as he saw her, he came a little way to meet her and it was then Alice noticed that he was *chained* to his desk.

'What can we do for you, Miss?' he cried, politely rubbing his hands.

'I was hoping to see the DIND,' Alice replied.

At this moment her attention was diverted by half a dozen creatures sitting close by, smoking cigars with their feet on the table and telling funny stories.

'Who are those?' she inquired.

'That's my party,' he returned.

'What? A *tea*-party?' suggested Alice.

'No, a *key*-party,' said he.

Alice thought this over for a minute, but gave it up.

'They don't appear to have much to do,' she ventured.

'Not now, not *now*,' conceded the Little Man, 'but you wait till the key changes. We'll all be awfully busy then.'

'But what key?' asked Alice, thoroughly dazed.

'Oh, don't you know the keys?' he cried; 'let me introduce you. There they are,' and he pointed towards a row of flat-looking objects with square bodies. Alice took them at first for a pack of cards, only, instead of a few pips, they had a great many letters inscribed on them. 'This is Gamma A,' went on the Little Man, selecting a common-looking fellow who was simply plastered all over with monograms.

'Whatever are these monograms?' inquired Alice.

'They're *not* monograms, my dear,' said Gamma A, 'they're bigrams.'

'But what are they for?'

'Code and Decode,' he replied. 'What's your name?'

'Alice,' said she, taken aback.

'Well now,' he explained, 'if I called you Alice that would be Gamma Punkt, but if I called you Gertrude that would be a Code. On the other hand, if I called Gertrude Alice, that would be a Decode.'

'Still, it would be much simpler to call me Alice,' she insisted.

'You've forgotten there's a War on,' he cried reproachfully. 'Of course,' he went on immediately, 'if I coded you, you wouldn't be you any longer, you'd be something else.'

'How?' asked Alice.

'You'd be classed according to your group. – What is her group, Kalamazoo?' he shouted to a broad, stunted fellow who appeared to consist chiefly of a mouth in which a row of teeth were arranged diagonally. The creature addressed opened its jaws and, looking inside, she saw

Alice – ASES.

'Well,' went on Gamma A, 'AS is AB and ES is UN. There you are, you see. ABUN. You're a bun.'

'What sort of bun?' she queried, bewildered.

'A colon,' he said. 'Why everyone knows that, even without asking Kalamazoo.'

'But a colon *isn't* a bun,' protested Alice, who felt inclined to burst into tears.

'Yes it is,' he insisted. 'Anyway it is in *this* room. It's a circular bun with two currants in it, one above –' But at this moment he was seized with convulsions, his pips faded into nothingness and he fell, a blank card, on to the table.

'The key's changed, the key's changed!' yelled the Little Man, jumping up immediately and losing his head; and all the Key Party took up the cry.

'We must go to bed!' went on the Little Man feverishly. – 'All of us! – at once! – Bring in the beds, bring in the beds!' and Alice saw the Old Gentleman, with a Boy Scout to help him, drag five beds, one after the other, into the room.

'Where's my bed? Where's *my* bed?' shrieked the Little Man, purple in the face with excitement.

'Over there, sir,' answered the Old Gentleman.

'Bring it here, bring it here at once. Don't you know I mustn't leave this table!' and he had the bed brought quite close.

'Why on earth are you all going to bed?' asked Alice, when the noise had subsided a little.

'We always do,' he explained, 'for the first forty-eight hours when the key changes.'

'But why not go home then?'

'Oh, that would never do. You see, if we went home for the *first* forty-eight hours, we shouldn't be able to take the *next* forty-eight hours off.'

By this time five of the creatures were already between the sheets. Only one of the Party, a tall ghost-like apparition with an eye-glass, sat working in the corner.

'Now mind you,' the White Rabbit admonished the Ghost, as he tucked himself in, 'mind you have the key ready by the time I wake up, for me to take to the DIND,' and he tucked his head under the bed-clothes.

In less than no time there was not a sound to be heard in the room, except for the ticking of the clock and the snores of the animals. Then the door opened and the Housemaid entered noiselessly. She was tall and handsome and beautifully dressed.

'Now is mein chance gome,' she muttered softly. 'I vill take de bull by de horn,' and she began tidying the papers and books into little heaps. Then she dusted the chairs, and then she began to sweep the floor.

'Aren't you afraid of spoiling your nice clothes?' whispered Alice.

'Ach no,' came the guttural reply. 'I had once twenty-three suits, but now dat I uniform to vear have, must I my gloth my goat to suit cut.'

At this moment the Little Man suddenly sat up in bed. He was blushing bright red to the roots of his hair, which was bristling on end.

'Dat is a sure sign,' the Housemaid explained to Alice, nodding in his direction, 'dat a senior officer is goming.'

Almost before she had finished speaking, a trumpet sounded and the door flew open. At the same time all the creatures woke up and jumped to their feet.

'It's the DIND, the DIND,' they shouted in chorus.

'What does DIND mean?' Alice asked the Little Man.

'Ssh!' he whispered. 'It's French, you know.'

At this moment an imposing figure strutted into the room between two other creatures, scarcely less impressive.

'Who are his companions?' Alice asked in an undertone.

'They're his Banks,' answered the Little Man.

'Banks!' ejaculated Alice.

'Yes, – he's always between them, you know – like a river.'

'Oh, I see. I thought you meant *money* banks.'

'I might have,' vaguely muttered the Little Man, who was by now trembling with excitement.

Alice noticed that the coats of the DIND and his followers were covered with little flags, and that, suspended by a ribbon from the DIND's neck, was a whole trayful of yet more flags. The DIND kept picking them up and sticking them into the chests of the two Banks.

'Is it a flag-day?' asked Alice. But no one paid any attention to her. They were all watching the DIND, who by now stood opposite the creature seated at the tube.

'You see,' said the DIND briskly to his friends, 'this is the fellow who gets out the keys.'

'Please, I'm the tubist,' protested the creature humbly.

'There, I told you so! That's just what I said. He gets them out of the tube.'

'Wonderful!' exclaimed the Right Bank.

'Marvellous!' echoed the Left Bank.

Whereupon the DIND took two more flags out of the tray and pinned them one on each of the two Banks.

'Hm, hm, hm!' coughed the White Rabbit, who had been following the DIND very closely since he came in.

'Yes?' inquired the DIND, wheeling round. 'Ah, it's the White Rabbit. How are you getting on?'

'Please,' began the White Rabbit, 'I believe I've got the hang of this now,' and he held out a piece of paper on which a lot of letters were written backwards and a lot of numbers upside down.

'You see, it seems to be a chi on an anagram, followed by transposition and substitution.'

'Transubstantiation! That's it,' cried the DIND. 'Exactly! I knew it. I said so all along.'

'Marvellous!' exclaimed the Right Bank.

'Wonderful!' echoed the Left Bank.

And, while the DIND was looking the other way, they each stole another flag from the tray.

'Capital, capital. Very good indeed!' went on the DIND to the White Rabbit. 'You really must have a flag.' And he began to select one from those in the basket.

Quickly the Banks exchanged surreptitious glances.

'One moment,' they whispered, as they tapped the DIND's arm. Then one of them drew from his pocket a little box, labelled:

For Other People

and below:

O.B.E.

He handed it to the DIND, who opened it and took out a claret-coloured flag.

'There you are,' said the DIND, as he stuck it into the White Rabbit. Then he turned round and shouted: 'Where is Captain James? I want to see Captain James.'

'He'll be in in a minute,' piped the Mouse hopefully as she looked at the clock, which stood at 6.49. 'His hours are 10 to 7 and 7 to 10,' she added wearily.

'Then why isn't he here now?' inquired the DIND impatiently.

'It isn't *quite* ten minutes to seven,' she ventured.

'What's that got to do with it?'

'Why, everything,' explained the Mouse patiently. 'I said that was one of his hours. You see, he's nearly always here at ten minutes to seven in the evening, and sometimes at seven minutes to ten in the morning.'

'But it's past ten to seven now,' cried the DIND, looking at his watch.

'Then it must be his day off,' sighed the Mouse with an air of finality. 'And that reminds me,' she went on, 'I'd quite forgotten what I came in for. – The War's over.'

A wave of consternation swept through the room. Here and there a silly creature attempted to cheer, but was promptly suppressed.

'There are these papers to fill in,' added the Mouse, handing them round to everybody. Alice took one and read:

*Questions.*

1. Do you want to go?
or 2. Do you want to stay?
or 3. Both. If so, state which.

Alice, looking over the shoulders of the animals as they wrote their answers, noticed that most of them left the first two spaces blank and wrote 'Which' in large letters in the third space, while a few, who liked to be on the safe side, scrawled 'Yes and No' against all three questions.

'What's it all about?' Alice asked the Mouse.

'It's demobilization,' she replied.

'Demobilization! Demobilization!' whispered the animals to each other with horror, and they began running aimlessly in all directions, hiding under the tables and saying their prayers, until one of them jumped on to a chair and began wailing something in a piercing voice. Gradually the others joined in until the chant became a chorus. Alice tried to make out the words of the song, but it sounded a hopeless jumble. It went something like this:

Oh, if a time should ever come when we're demobilized,
How we shall miss the interests which once our life comprised!
We shall not sleep 'mid dirty sheets, 'neath unwashed counterpanes,
Nor hear the Colonel chatter more than all his aeroplanes.
We shall not ask of Somers Cox how much he pays per spat,
Nor muddle Measures Roter Kliff with Measures Hubert Gat.
No breakfasting on Ersatz egg and Admiralty food,
No 'Heute Nacht und Morgen Früh Angriff auf England Süd.'
We shall not plot directionals, nor work at endless sums,
Nor haste to finish off our baths before Miss Roddam comes.
No marvelling at fouler smells than any we have met.
No 'Wegen schlechten Wetters es wird nicht gearbeitet.'
We shall not ask why Bullough went to visit Schillig Roads,
Nor Mrs Bailey why she chose her capillary modes.
No 'F.T. Ubung heute Nacht auf ungedämpften Wellen,'
No 'Unterseebootssicherung für Iste Treffen stellen,'
We'll wonder not what Green has paid to keep his father drunk,
Nor try to prove to Jellicoe the 'Rheinland' was not sunk.
No further nights at the Savoy in luxury Sicilian,
No wrestling with 'Torpedobootszerstörerhalbflottillem.'
We shall not wear mysterious airs nor boast what we could blab,
Nor chase the solitary soap across the slippery slab.
No more delights like these for us:- But *Denniston* will *never*
Desert his solitary post:- *He* will go on for ever!

When the song had died away, the Mouse, who had been looking through the papers, was heard to say: 'It's all nonsense. Some of you will *have* to go.'

But immediately they began hissing and booing and shouting louder and louder: 'We *won't* be demobilized! We *won't* be demobilized!'

'Well, it's no use being silly,' said the Mouse sensibly as soon as she could make herself heard. 'Somebody's *got* to go. You can choose who it is.'

'We *none* of us want to go,' they all cried together, and then one of them suddenly pointed to Alice and yelled inconsequently: 'Anyway, who's she?'

Whereupon all the animals shrieked with one voice: 'Yes, who's *she*? We don't want *her*. Let *her* go.'

'Oh, do be quiet,' cried Alice angrily, stopping her ears. But they only bellowed the louder: 'Demobilize the child! Demobilize the child!' and began to surge towards her.

Alice by now was thoroughly disgusted with them.

'If you touch me,' she cried, 'I'll tell you all what I think of you. I'll tell you the truth.'

'No, no, not the truth!' they screamed immediately, shrinking away from her in terror. 'Not that. Anything but that. If you tell the truth it's all over.'

But Alice was thoroughly wound up.

'I *will* tell you,' she shouted, 'and I don't care *what* happens. You're only a lot of common, callous, crooked, cranky, crotchety, cattish, carping, critical, cracked, cross, contemptible, cantankerous creatures.'

# Appendix

*Parody of* Jabberwocky *by Dilly Knox concerning the 'clever mathematicians' working in Hut 6 at Bletchley Park during World War Two.*

Dilly Knox's codebreaking was as successful in World War Two as when he told Alice about breaking the hand cipher 'three letter stuff' in I.D.25. He saw breaking the Enigma machine as slaying the Jabberwock and in his Saxon account of how it was done, he gives due credit to Alan Turing 'my bombe-ish boy' who dealt the final blow. In Frank Birch's Naval Section, Hut 4, the linguists were known to translate Carroll's *Jabberwocky* poem into various languages during spare time on their watches. His nonsense and the gibberish they had to spend their waking hours in unravelling had much in common.

At the end of the real *Wonderland* story Alice and the King of Hearts had a conversation about the frustration of trying to make sense of all the lines of gibberish received from the Knave of Hearts.

'I don't believe there is an atom of meaning in it,' said Alice.

'If there's no meaning in it,' said the King, 'that saves us a world of trouble, you know, as we needn't try to find any ... and, yet I don't know ... I seem to see some meaning in them after all.'

\*\*\*

'Twas HUTSIX, and the WRANGLERCOVES
Did twist and twiddle at the CYC;
All grimst were the JEFFREYBROWS,
And the BABBAGE outschreik.

'Beware the SEVENTHWHEEL, my son,
The pale FULLHOUSE, the NETZ that fail;
Move not the UMKEHRWALZE, and shun
The UNCONFIRMED FEMALE.'

He took the COTTAGECROWD in HAND,
Oft times the REGISTRATORS sought;
Then 'midst his CILLIS, SLUGS and SNAKES,
He sat awhile in thought.

And, as they over FOSSSHEETS groan,
A REDHOTTIP (with wheels to name)
Came TURING through the telephone.
And DILLIED as it came!

4, 5 and 2! No more ado –
The RINGSTELLUNG. Turn wheels about.

Still doubt appal, but STECKER fall
Uncontradicted out.

'And hast thou truly BROKE the BLUE?
Come to the STORE, my BOMBE-ISH boy!
Fetch JOSH, KITS, BOLS, AARD, CERA, WALTZ.'
He LUFTGAUED in his joy.

'Twas HUTSIX, and the WRANGLERCOVES
Did twist and twiddle at the CYC;
All grimset were the JEFFREYBROWS,
And the BABBAGE outschreik.

With thanks to The Lewis Carroll Society,
Flat 11 Eastfields, 24–30 Victoria Road North, Southsea PO5 1PU.

www.lewiscarrollsociety.org.uk

Text © the Frank Birch, Dilly Knox, and G.P. Mackeson Estates.
Introductions © Mavis Batey and Edward Wakeling.

Images courtesy of the Bletchley Park Trust, except for the following: The Estate of
Nigel de Grey: p.10; Edward Wakeling: pp.15, 32, 38, 59; Alamy: pp.16, 17, 20; Churchill
Archives Centre, The Papers of Alexander Guthrie Denniston, DENN 3/2/4, 3/2/3,
3/3/45: pp.24, 26, 54; ShaunArmstrong/mubsta.com: p.60; John Tenniel (public
domain) via Wikimedia Commons: p.61.

ISBN 978-1-84165-663-2      1/21

Pitkin Publishing, Pavilion Books Ltd, 43 Great Ormond Street, London, WC1N 3HZ.